RED HERRING MYSTERIES

Level 2
Solving Mysteries Through
Critical Questioning

SERIES TITLES
Red Herring Mysteries
Level 1
Level 2

Written By
Thomas Camilli

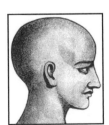

© 2008
THE CRITICAL THINKING CO.™
www.CriticalThinking.com
Phone: 800-458-4849 • Fax: 831-393-3277
P.O. Box 1610 • Seaside • CA 93955-1610
ISBN 978-1-60144-163-8

TABLE OF CONTENTS

About This Book

The activities in this book are designed to improve your students' problem-solving skills and refine their ability to apply logical deductive reasoning. To accomplish these, students are given the opportunity to solve puzzling mysteries in much the same way as a real detective—by asking probing questions and forming conclusions based upon the answers.

These activities can also help to change the way your students think. For example, the solution to some of the mysteries may require students to alter stereotyped sex roles or recognize the multiple meanings of key words.

How It Works

Each of the "mysteries" on these pages is part of a longer untold story which is "behind the scenes." It is up to the students to deduce the rest of the story from clues derived from answers to their questions.

For example, the story behind the sentence, "If Leo had kept his hand down he might be a free man today," can eventually be revealed if enough questions are asked and the answers are used to form a mental image of the event.

It may take many questions over several days to finally reveal that Leo is a not-too-bright bank robber who incriminates himself at his trial by raising his hand when the prosecutor asks a witness, "Is the person who robbed the bank present in the courtroom today?"

The Rules of the Game

The rules for these activities are simple.

- Students must phrase their questions so that the answer is either yes or no.

- You should try to answer questions with only a yes or no (occasionally a maybe or sometimes can be given as an appropriate response).

- You may give hints to redirect thinking or stimulate new questions.

Behind the Scenes

The solutions to these mysteries are found at the back of this book. It is important to visualize the scenario of the mystery before you begin a questioning session. That way you can answer questions based upon your personal mental image of what has taken place. After visualizing the scene, you may find that you need to alter it slightly to suit your geographic locale or your students' cultural backgrounds.

Suggestions for Use

As a motivator or time filler: These detective mysteries can be used as five-minute warm-up or sponge activities to begin or end a class period.

As a cooperative activity: Students can be divided into teams. Limiting the number of questions that a team is allowed to ask keeps one group from dominating the session. Each team may ask only one question per round, and the questions may be asked only by the team's spokesperson. This helps to eliminate frivolous questions. (In fact, many students will learn quickly how to narrow the search for important clues by asking comprehensive questions.)

Another method for limiting questioning is to pass out coupons to the groups before each session. A coupon is collected before each question is answered. When the group runs out of coupons, the group is out of that questioning session.

As a writing activity: Questions may be submitted only in writing. Questions are read and answered at the beginning or end of class. To prevent students who already know the answer from spoiling the activity for others, possible solutions should also be submitted only in writing.

To develop critical listening skills: After a few practice rounds, a new rule could be imposed: repeat questions will not be answered. This causes students to listen more carefully to each other's questions and answers.

Critical listening and recall is improved if the students are allowed to remark (with a noise or a word) when a question is a repeat of one that has already been asked.

As a lesson in critical thinking: Like all good mystery stories, the ones in this book have vivid plots, settings, and characters. Questioning strategies can be improved by finding areas of the stories that have not been thoroughly addressed. By analyzing individual questions and suggesting ways to improve them, you can increase students' critical thinking ability.

Tips

- Limiting the number of questions allowed during a session tends to improve the quality of the questions.

- Choosing a student to present the story and answer the questions allows you to model inquiry techniques by taking an active part in the activity. Instead of simply describing how to formulate good questions, you can then guide the students by demonstrating higher level thinking and questioning techniques.

- It is important to summarize the clues that have already been discovered before continuing an interrupted questioning session. This refreshes students' memories and updates students who may have been absent during a questioning session. One of the best ways to do this is to ask the students what they remember about the story and what clues have already been revealed.

Using the Mystery Pages

The pages in this book are designed for multiple uses.

- Reproducing the mystery page on transparency material and using it every time the story is investigated helps students who have a limited auditory memory.

- Summarizing what the students already know about the mystery and writing it on the transparency will help those students with learning difficulties to continue to participate in the questioning activity.

- Letting everyone see the actual mystery message permits students to analyze the wording of the mystery for possible clues.

- Using the mystery page as a poster in your room will serve to remind you and your students of both the activity and the mystery in progress.

Using the Graphic Organizers

A variety of graphic organizers could be used to help students with the thinking process. Two are supplied with this text. Here are some ways that they can be used:

For cooperative learning: Before beginning the questioning session, each group receives one copy of the mystery story and a copy of the graphic organizers. Encourage them to use the graphic organizers to arrange a questioning strategy. At the end of the session the group members can map out on the organizer the direction in which the answers are leading and plan the next questioning strategies.

Modeling the thinking process: Using a transparency of Organizer #1, select a mystery and model the process of analyzing the story for clues. Are there any words in the story that could have multiple meanings? Are there any clues about the setting, characters, or action of the story? From the first reading of the mystery, what are some possible solutions?

Guided practice: Individually or in cooperative groups, students could use Organizer #1 to help them analyze the wording of a mystery story. They could contribute their ideas about the mystery before beginning the questioning session.

Summarizing: Organizer #2 can be used to list the clues that have been discovered from previous questioning sessions.

The Questioning Process

To give you a better understanding of how to use these mystery stories to develop critical thinking, here is an abbreviated script of a questioning session with a group of students.

The teacher in this example uses several strategies to get the students to think in new and different directions without giving away the premise of the story. You might want to use similar strategies with your students to get them back on track if they get stuck or start pursuing a nonproductive line of questioning.

Teacher: "We're going to try to solve a mystery today. I know the entire story behind this mystery, but I am only going to let you in on a small part of it to begin with. It will be up to you to figure out the rest of the story as a detective would, by asking good questions, listening carefully to the answers, and putting clues together to form a mental picture of what is happening.

"Here are some rules that must be followed. You may ask me any question as long as it is phrased so that my answer can be a yes or a no. Listen to the questions that others ask because you may pick up clues from my answers to their questions. Try not to repeat questions that others have already asked.

"I will attempt to answer your questions with only a yes or a no. Sometimes that is difficult to do, so I may give more than a one-word answer to some questions. Listen to the way that I answer yes or no. That may give you a clue to the solution of the mystery or help you phrase your next question.

"Do you understand the rules? If not, be sure to ask for an explanation. OK, here is the mystery story: (the teacher places the transparency of the story on the overhead). It reads, 'Although she was not an unusually large person, people were constantly amazed at what Livia weighed.'"

Student: "What do you mean? Who is she? Is she really a big person?"

Teacher: "That's what you are supposed to find out by asking questions. If you ask enough questions, you can find out exactly what is happening here. Try it. Remember, your questions must be phrased so that I can answer them with yes or no."

Student: "Who is she?"

Teacher: "I can't answer that question the way it is asked. Please rephrase the question so that I can answer it with a yes or a no."

Student: "Is she a person?"

Teacher: "Yes. That's a good question. Why do you think it is a good question?"

Student: "The word she could mean lots of things. It could stand for an animal, like a lioness. Sometimes ships are called she."

Student: "When the story says that people were constantly amazed at what she weighed, does that mean that she was a really large person?"

Teacher: "No one said that she was a large person. You have to listen carefully to the way the story is told for clues to the mystery. Now, how is the story worded? Read it carefully because every word counts."

Student: "How can she be a small person and still weigh a lot—enough that people were amazed at her?"

Teacher: "I can't answer until your thought is posed as a question."

Student: "Is she a weight lifter? Does she compete in the Olympics?"

Teacher: "That's two questions. I can only answer one at a time."

Student: "OK, is Livia a weight lifter?"

Teacher: "No."

Student: "Does this have anything to do with how many pounds she weighs?"

Teacher: "No. Good question."

Student: "Does weigh mean that she weighs things for other people, you know like a butcher weighs meat for other people?"

Teacher: "No."

Student: "Does she weigh big things, like trucks or elephants?"

Teacher: "No."

Student: "Does the word weigh have anything to do with finding the mass of an object?"

Teacher: "No. But why is that a good question?"

Student: "It eliminates a lot of things with just one question."

Student: "Is Livia a judge?"

Teacher: "Before I answer your question, what made you think of that?"

Student: "Well, judges sometimes have to weigh the evidence in a case to reach a decision."

Teacher: "That's good thinking. Another use for the work weigh. I'm sorry, but the answer is no. Did that question start any of you thinking in a different direction?"

Student: "Yes, it makes me see that words can have more than one meaning."

Student: "Would it help to know what Livia does for a living?"

Teacher: "Yes."

Student: "Does Livia drive a truck?"

Teacher: "No."

Student: "Is she an airline pilot?"

Teacher: "No. Can you think of some questions that could narrow down what she does without having to go through all the occupations in the world?"

Student: "Does she work indoors?"

Teacher: "That's a good question. It covers a whole group of occupations with one question. The answer is no."

Student: "Can we then assume that she works outdoors?"

Teacher: "A good detective never assumes anything. They question every assumption to get at the truth."

Student: "Does Livia work outdoors?"

Teacher: "Yes."

Student: "Does she work on land?"

Teacher: "No."

Student: "Does she work at sea?"

Teacher: "Yes."

Student: "Does she work on a ship?"

Teacher: "Yes."

Student: "Oh, I think I know the answer!"

Teacher: "If you think you know, ask a question that will help others to discover the answer."

Student: "Does Livia work mostly when the ship enters and leaves port?"

Teacher: "Yes."

Student: "Does the word weigh have something to do with a part of the ship?"

Teacher: "Yes. I think you are close to the solution. Ask another question"

Student: "Is Livia in charge of raising and lowering the anchor on a ship?"

Teacher: "Yes. That's it!"

Student: "Huh?"

Teacher: "Livia handles the controls that raise and lower the massive anchor on the ship. She weighs it. In this case, the word weigh means to raise something. Can you see how people would be constantly amazed at what Livia weighed?

"Now, do you think you understand how these mystery stories work? Well, here's another one for you to try to solve. If we don't have time to complete it today, we'll work on it when we have some time left over tomorrow or the next day."

Levels of Difficulty

The mystery stories in this book have been leveled according to the amount of difficulty students will have reaching the solution. The stories in the beginning of the book are easier for the average class to deduce than those farther back. The first two or three stories are excellent to use when modelling the questioning process needed to solve the remainder of the mysteries.

Many stories in the last third of this book are complicated and will require a much longer period of time to solve. You may have to give more clues and actively guide your students' thinking as they work through some of the more difficult mystery stories.

Extending Activities

After students have experience solving the mysteries in this book, ask them to create their own stories. Sources for story ideas are mystery programs on television and unusual stories from magazines, mystery novels, or the newspaper.

The best mysteries are those which contain words that have more than one meaning. For example, a story could be one floor in a tall building, or it could be a written or spoken composition. A stroke could have something to do with the brain, or it could be a term that describes a tennis or golf swing. Try to incorporate these kinds of words into the story.

Mystery Story: _____

_____

_____

(1) Words in the story which have multiple meanings:

Word: _____ Meanings: _____

Word: _____ Meanings: _____

Word: _____ Meanings: _____

Word: _____ Meanings: _____

What clues can you find in the words of the mystery story?

Setting clues	Character clues	Action clues
_____	_____	_____
_____	_____	_____
_____	_____	_____
_____	_____	_____
_____	_____	_____
_____	_____	_____

Possible Solutions:

_____

_____

_____

_____

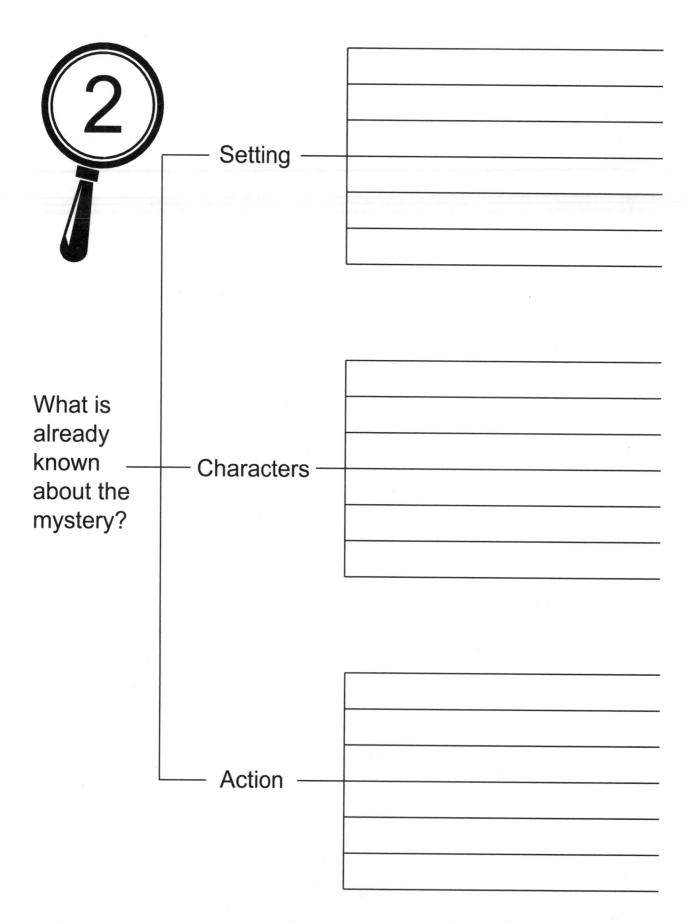

What is already known about the mystery?

Setting

Characters

Action

A used car salesman told his customer that the car she was buying was covered by a bumper-to-bumper, roof-to-road, unlimited one-year warranty on all parts and labor.

When the car broke down three months later, the woman found that she had to personally pay for all the repairs. Why?

Tony and Bibi fell in love and became engaged.

One day while they were on an outing, Tony deliberately pulled off Bibi's ring and dropped it into the lake.

Bibi was very happy about that and shouted, "Thank you!" to Tony as loudly as she could.

The O'Grady twins had very unusual first names. When asked about them, the twins' mother replied that her brother was mostly responsible for choosing their names.

What did she mean by that?

Two attorneys were engaged in a heated argument with each other and with the judge. As a result of the argument, one of the attorneys began suffering from a terrible stroke.

Although dozens of spectators were present at the time, none of them came to the attorney's aid. Why?

Jesse is known to thousands of people as an intelligent and hard-working man.

Although raised in the alleys of his town, his perseverance and skill has taken him from the gutters to a position of importance and prestige.

What does Jesse do?

Haroun has a problem. He has seven pieces of fruit to divide among his eight friends.

To be fair, he wants each friend to receive a nearly equal amount of fruit and have none left over. To further compound his problem, the fruit is all different sizes.

How does Haroun solve his problem?

When asked what she wanted to do when she grew up, Liang replied, "I want to sit all day long on a bench near the park." Liang's parents were very pleased with her aspirations. Why?

The body of a man clothed only in a swimsuit was found among the branches high up in a tree. Investigators were at first baffled by the discovery, but soon solved the mystery surrounding the man's death.

What was their solution?

Although she ran from her pursuer with all her might, she was relieved when he finally caught up with her on the narrow path.

When her son asked her how her hands stayed so soft, she replied, "I owe it all to Greasoff dishwashing liquid."

The young boy was confused because he had never seen Greasoff being used at his home.

What could his mother have meant?

Two men both claimed to be the missing heir to a millionaire's fortune.

The executor of the estate proposed a simple test to prove which of the men was the true heir.

When one of the men readily agreed to the test, the executor immediately knew that he was the impostor.

How?

While relaxing on the deck outside her cabin one summer evening, Vivian fell into a deep trance-like sleep.

When she awoke, she felt as if she had slept only an hour or two, but it was now the middle of winter.

How could this be?

While preparing for an important speech, the senator went to a quiet room offstage to practice.

When asked by a passerby, "Are you nervous about giving this speech?" the senator replied, "No, not at all."

The passerby knew that the senator was not telling the truth. How?

Morton the Magnificent, Magician Extraordinaire, boasted that he could escape from anything. Then one day a member of the audience helped him get into something from which he couldn't escape no matter what he tried. What was it?

An inventor boasted that he had discovered a way to break something without touching it in any way with anything.

He assured his friends that if they would come to his laboratory that very evening, he would happily demonstrate his discovery to them.

They did and he did. What happened?

Bonnie has an interesting job. She spends much of her work time outdoors, gets plenty of exercise, and meets lots of interesting men.

Her boss even encourages her to whistle while she works.

What job does Bonnie do?

A bank robbery is committed in front of dozens of witnesses. The robber is eventually arrested and brought to trial. Although he is positive that the person is guilty, the judge is forced to dismiss the charges. Why?

No matter what the director tried, the actors still refused to perform. Why?

If she had followed her
mother's advice she might
still be alive.

After listening to her teacher tell the fables associated with George Washington's youth, Marsha became convinced that at least one of the things George did could never be repeated today. What was that feat, and why can't it be repeated?

Working alone late at night, a biologist accidentally discovered something which could be in a container of water for hours without it getting the least bit wet.

When she shared her discovery with her peers, they chuckled at her in amusement.

What did she discover?

There are three children in the Spiff family, two boys named Large and Medium, and a girl named 7 and 3/4. Although the names were unusual, friends of the Spiffs never gave them a second thought. Why?

Relying on an expert's opinion, an antique collector purchased a rare object. Later, upon closer inspection, it became obvious that the object was a crude fake. What was the object, and how was the collector duped?

If Gwen had heeded the warning, she might be a free woman today.

Asked what he would like to be when he grew up, Alex replied, "I want to follow in my uncle's footsteps and be a policeman."

His mother thought it was an odd statement, because Alex's uncle had always said that he wanted nothing to do with law enforcement.

What could Alex have meant?

If he had kept his hand down, Leo might be a free man today.

A woman realized that she was becoming hard of hearing, and she knew that she couldn't afford a hearing aid.

When a friend became aware of her problem, she suggested an inexpensive alternative that helped the woman to hear more clearly.

What did the friend suggest?

Although it had nothing to do with safety, Spike always avoided traveling by ship. Why?

In desperation, an elderly woman surreptitiously entered an unlocked home. As a direct result of her actions while inside the home, she became a millionaire.

What happened?

A man and his wife returned home after work to find their dog lying on the floor, choking. Concerned about the dog's health, the man took the dog to the veterinarian.

A half-hour later, the woman's husband phoned her shouting, "Get out of the house immediately! I have already called the police."

What was happening?

At first readers were disturbed by the headline, "Hunter rewarded for shooting rare and endangered animals," but after reading the article they understood the hunter's motives.

Delia bet a friend that she could remain underwater without the aid of artificial breathing devices for more than an hour. Early one morning she proved it to her friend and won her bet. How did she do it?

Angelo's doctor told him that the only sure cure for his illness was not to take anything for it. What was wrong with Angelo?

A man walks into an office to apply for a job. Within minutes he is surrounded by police, handcuffed, and arrested. What happened?

He might have eluded his pursuers had he remembered an old saying. What happened, and what was the saying?

Benny's parents were convinced that Benny, already a famous and well-liked public figure, someday would go down in history for what he was doing. What was that?

Although Will and Thelma had only recently become engaged, their friends were convinced that their marriage would surely end up on the rocks. Why?

Nearly hysterical, Kim called her parents and told them that because of what she had done, both her life and her career were in ruins. Her parents had been expecting this to happen to Kim and were not surprised by her news. Why?

Given an expensive gift by admiring fans, the actress replied, "Thank you. I'll never part with it." Her remarks brought boos from some of her fans. Why?

Although Gwen and Pat were not related, their friends were struck by the likeness between them. How can that be?

Before passing sentence, the judge asked the defendant if any lesson had been learned as a result of the trial. The defendant replied, "Yes, I've learned to stop exaggerating!" What was meant by the remark?

The sign on the window read, "What we achieve: remains to be seen." What goes on inside?

The newspaper headline read, "Cross-country marathon has photo finish." What happened here?

It collapsed when the chain broke. What was it?

Suddenly losing her balance, she tumbled from the top of the ladder. Shaken, but uninjured by the fall, she immediately started climbing again. What happened?

Although well known for his writing, in his entire career he had actually never completed a sentence. How can that be?

When confronted with a choice between summer jobs, Lyn decided to wait rather than embark on something that might wind up being over her head. What were her job choices? Which one did she choose and why?

Lalo informed his parents that when he grew up he wanted to "become a humanitarian who dedicated his life to serving mankind." His parents were disappointed with his decision. Why?

Feeling beat at the end of a day of hard work, Ali looked around for a chair. Finding none, she angrily did something that landed her behind bars for the rest of her life. What happened?

Although the forecast of 120 degrees in the shade was accurate, none of the participants seemed to be bothered by the temperature. Why?

Deciding that it was about time, Gwen gave her new pet a very appropriate name. What was it?

While on her summer vacation, Beth visited a quiet place where the air was chilly and leaves were turning. It was there that she discovered the true meaning of rest and relaxation. Where did she go?

Although he was extremely good at his scientific discoveries, he gained fame for his ability to make new friends. Who was he?

A woman entered a business and purchased a number of objects. She then went to similar businesses in two other cities and did exactly the same thing. Why?

Some motorists stopped at a roadblock were surprised at what the police asked them to do. What was it, and why were they asked to do it?

The newspaper announced that the ceremonies would take place at noon, 2:15, 4:30, 6:45, and 9:00 P.M. What were the ceremonies?

Throughout the match a highly capable contestant consistently missed short, easy shots. Why was this happening?

The reason he gave the press for leaving his job was illness and fatigue. That wasn't exactly the truth and it wasn't exactly a lie. Why did he leave?

Although her explanation was unusual, it convinced the judge to reverse her conviction. What had she done, and what was her explanation?

"Help wanted afternoons and evenings. Must have an enchanting voice and a charming personality. An excellent memory is essential. Some cooking involved. Should be good at spelling." What is the job and why must the prospective employee have these qualifications?

Although positive that Calvin was the ringleader, the principal found it difficult to actually pin anything on the elusive young man. Why?

They might have succeeded if he hadn't tried to make a clean getaway.

Although the audience had enjoyed the performance, they booed the star at the end of the show. Why?

When the investigators arrived, they found the victims slouched at a table. One had been hit repeatedly with large clubs. The other victim, who had also been hit with a club, was found to have two matching diamonds in his hand. It did not take long for the investigators to figure out what happened. What happened?

Behind The Scenes

1. The salesman lied, and the woman never got the guarantee in writing.

2. Tony and Bibi are skydivers. On one skydiving outing, Bibi's parachute "D" ring was somehow blown back behind her and she couldn't reach it. Tony pulled it for her, then dropped it so that he could pull his own parachute ring. In relief. The ring fell into a lake. Bibi yelled, "Thank you!" to her friend who had already fallen below her.

3. Mrs. O'Grady's brother had a problem remembering names. He suggested that she call her fraternal twins the only names he was sure to remember. She complied and named her daughter Deniece and her son Denephew.

4. The attorneys were opponents in a tennis match. They argued with each other and with the line judge over what one of them thought was a bad call. As a result of the argument, one player became so angry that it began to affect his swing (tennis stroke).

5. Jesse is a famous professional bowler. He is so busy now that he has little time to spare.

6. The fruit that Haroun has is apples. He decided that the only way to evenly divide the apples among his eight friends was to cut them up and bake them in an apple pie.

7. Liang Trang is an Asian immigrant who just became an American citizen. Although she did not know a lot of English, she tried to communicate that she wanted to be a judge (to be appointed to the bench). The courthouse where she would like to work is next to the public park.

8. The body was found in the topmost branches of a tall pine tree. There had been a forest fire nearby. Water-dropping helicopters were being used to fight the fire. The helicopters were refilling their giant water buckets by dipping them into a nearby lake. Unknown to the pilot, a swimmer in the lake was drawn into the bucket and dropped onto the fire. The investigators surmised this when they learned that the man had died from drowning.

9. The girl is running the anchor leg of a relay race. Her team is ahead, and she is relieved when the runner behind her catches up and successfully passes the baton.

10. The boy's mother is an actress who appears on Greasoff dishwashing liquid commercials. She has made enough money doing soap commercials to hire a housekeeper who cooks, cleans, and washes the dishes for her.

11. The executor knew a secret. The true heir had hemophilia, a rare blood disorder that causes almost uncontrollable bleeding.

   He proposed a blood test to the two potential heirs knowing that the real one would not allow his life to be threatened in this way. When the unknowing impostor agreed to the test, the executor knew which man was the authentic heir.

12. Vivian was on the patio of her first class cabin on a cruise ship. She fell asleep

just before the ship crossed the equator on a trip from Hawaii to New Zealand.

The equator is the dividing line between opposite seasons. She fell asleep north of the equator while in the middle of summer and awoke two hours later south of the equator in the middle of winter.

13. The senator, a woman, had retired to the restroom to practice her speech. In her flustered state, she didn't notice that she was in the men's restroom.

14. Trouble. The member of the audience assisted Morton with the commission of a crime for which he was eventually imprisoned.

15. An assurance is a kind of promise. The scientist did not show up that evening, thereby breaking his promise.

16. Bonnie is a referee for professional football.

17. The bank robber was a facially-disfigured fire victim who held up the bank to get money for plastic surgery. The operations were so successful that, although the police and the judge were positive that the suspect was guilty, none of the witnesses could identify her in a police lineup. The judge had to dismiss the case because of lack of evidence.

18. The "actors" were sea lions who were performing in a seal show at a marine life park. The park had been leased for the evening by a large corporation. The guests were all dressed in formal attire—women in white gowns and men in black tuxedos.

Hundreds of the guests attended the special performance of the sea lion show. The sea lions came out for the beginning of the show only to see an audience that had the same markings as killer whales, their most feared enemy. The sea lions scurried off the stage and no matter what the show's director tried, they refused to perform.

19. She was a musician who played the clarinet in a symphony orchestra. Because of her skill she had a position of importance in the orchestra. Another clarinet player, jealous of the woman's ability, murdered her just before a performance.

On the night of the murder, the woman's clarinet reeds were switched with reeds which had been soaked with an odorless and tasteless poison. As the woman licked the reed in her clarinet to make it pliable, she unknowingly ingested the poison. As the conductor began the first part of the performance, the woman slumped over dead.

The woman's mother had never liked that her daughter played the clarinet. She had often advised her to learn to play a more versatile instrument such as the piano. If the woman had followed her mother's advice, she might still be alive.

20. Marsha is a literal-thinking fourth grader. As a result of a conversation that she had with her father the night before, she became convinced that George Washington would find it utterly impossible to throw a silver dollar across the Potomac River today.

Marsha had asked her father for a raise in her allowance, and her father sympathized with her by telling her that today the dollar just doesn't go as far as it used to.

21. While working late at night the biologist became intrigued with the thought that the water in her aquarium was filled with light, but the light never got wet.

22. The parents of the Spiff children were not too bright. They thought that they would have a hard time coming up with names for their children until a friend suggested that they just pull the names out of a hat. Being literal thinkers, the Spiffs did just that.

23. Too vain to show that she needed glasses, the farsighted collector relied on the advice of an acquaintance who claimed to be an expert on antiquities. The collector bought a supposedly rare Roman coin from the reign of Julius Caesar. When she got home and put on her glasses, she realized that she had been taken. The "rare" coin was dated 44 B.C.!

24. Gwen is a professional safecracker. Although police were sure that she had committed a recent series of burglaries, they could never match her fingerprints to those on the safes. That's because Gwen opened safes using her toes instead of her fingers.

One day a barefooted Gwen became involved in a heated argument with a restaurant owner. The detectives who were tailing Gwen came to the owner's aid. One of the detectives noticed Gwen's bare feet and made a connection with the prints on the safe. Gwen was arrested and sent to prison.

The sign that Gwen did not heed was on the door of the restaurant. It read, "No shoes, no shirt, no service."

25. Alex's uncle was a bank robber who

was wanted by the police. His mother was embarrassed by her notorious relative, and Alex was determined to hunt him down (follow in his footsteps) and capture him. After that, he wanted to go into law enforcement to show his mother's friends that the entire family was not bad.

26. Leo was the defendant on trial for bank robbery. The prosecuting attorney was questioning a witness to the robbery. The prosecutor asked the witness if she could recognize the robber. When the witness answered in the affirmative, the prosecutor asked, "Is the person who robbed the bank present in the courtroom today?" At that point, the not-too-bright defendant raised his hand, admitting his guilt to the jury.

27. The woman's friend suggested that instead of a hearing aid, the woman buy a swimmer's earplug and place it in her bad ear. The woman's friend is a psychologist and knows about human nature. She knows that when a person communicates with someone who appears to be wearing a hearing aid, the person usually speaks louder and more clearly to the listener.

28. Spike was an avid card player, but alas he wasn't too bright. He refused to travel by ship when he became convinced that it would be impossible to play cards on one. He had heard that someone is always standing on the deck.

29. Walking down the sidewalk, the woman found herself desperately in need of a rest room. She entered a nearby funeral home to use theirs. Feeling peculiar about what she was doing, and wanting to look like a visiting mourner, the woman stepped into a room

containing the body of an elderly man and signed her name in the guest book before using the rest room.

Later that week she was contacted by the dead man's attorney and told that she had inherited the man's substantial fortune. It seems that he had willed his fortune to be divided equally among all the mourners who signed his guest book. She was the only one who had done so.

30. The veterinarian found that the dog had a human finger lodged in its throat. The man surmised that the dog had attacked an intruder who might still be in the house.

31. The "hunter" is an antique hunter, and the rare and endangered animals are carved wooden carousel animals. His photographs (shots) of carousel animals had been made into a top-selling book. The headline was designed to attract readers' attention to a review of the book.

32. Delia played a trick on her friend. She knew that time changes twice a year— back an hour in the fall and ahead an hour in the spring. She invited her friend to join her on the spring morning when the time advances an hour. She entered the pool at 1:59:45 A.M. that morning and emerged thirty seconds later. In the meantime the clock had advanced a whole hour, and it was then 3:00:15 A.M. Although she had really held her breath for less than a minute, she had technically held it for more than an hour.

33. Angelo is suffering from kleptomania, an almost uncontrollable urge to steal. His doctor, a psychiatrist, had been working with him to control the illness.

34. Seeking honest employment for the first time in his life, an illiterate criminal entered what he thought was an employment office. Unable to read anything for himself, he asked a person waiting in the office to read the announcements on the bulletin board. The only thing the person could make out from the distance was a newspaper headline that said, "Man wanted for armed robbery."

Thinking it was a help-wanted notice, the man excitedly went to the counter to apply. To prove he had the experience and qualifications necessary for the position, he boasted of successful armed robberies he had committed without getting caught. Unfortunately for him he was actually in the office of the District Attorney. He was arrested.

35. The old saying he should have remembered was, "Look before you leap." Trying to hide from pursuing police, a burglar leaped over the wall of a compound into a large park-like area filled with people. As it turned out, the police were able to easily recognize the clothed burglar among the startled nudists.

36. Benny was the popular quarterback of the champion high school football team. Believing that athletes didn't need to study in order to succeed, Benny began watching television every night instead of doing his homework. His parents knew that Benny's belief was wrong and were sure his grades would suffer as a result of his behavior. As it turned out, besides going down in history, he was also failing math and science.

37. Thelma had spent most of her life as a lighthouse keeper on a wave-

swept rocky outcropping on the coast. Thelma's friends convinced her that it would be appropriate, as well as quaint, to be wed on the rocky ledge at the base of the lighthouse.

38. Nearly hysterical with delight, Kim phoned her parents to tell them that she had accepted a position as professor of archaeology at a prestigious college. Her parents, both archaeologists themselves, always had confidence that Kim would get the position and were not surprised at her news.

39. In order to play her role in the stage production, the actress had to appear completely bald. As a gag, some of her loyal fans gave the actress a plaque with a gold-plated comb attached to it. The fans booed at the quick pun the actress came up with for her reply.

40. Gwen and Pat were admiring a large painting in a museum when an earthquake caused a portrait (a likeness of a person) located between them to fall off the wall onto two friends who were accompanying them.

41. The defendant had once complimented his wife by telling her that she was "One in a million." The man's wife had suspected for some time that her husband was being unfaithful to her. The remark caused her to think that the saying might have some truth to it. Upon investigating, she found that her husband was a bigamist with wives in several other states. She had him arrested, and he was punished for his crime.

42. The building houses a school for morticians. The students learn how to prepare the mortal remains of people to

be viewed one last time by their loved ones.

43. This has nothing to do with a foot race. Two pen pals living on opposite coasts had been carrying on a marathon (long term) correspondence romance with each other. It was only when they finally exchanged photos of each other that one of the correspondents called off the relationship. The photo she received was a recent one of her pen pal—with his wife and children. An article about their relationship later appeared in the newspaper.

44. "It" was the ecosystem of a pond which collapsed when there was a break in the food chain.

45. She was the chairperson and CEO of a large corporation. Implicated in an embezzlement scheme when the firm's books didn't balance at the end of the year, she was fired (she tumbled from the top of the corporate ladder).

Later acquitted of any crime, she immediately began her climb back to the top of the corporate ladder.

46. The man was a notorious forger, who although frequently imprisoned for his crimes had always been released before the end of his prison sentence.

47. Lyn's job choices were between waitressing and working as a canoe instructor at a summer camp. A literal thinker, she chose waitressing when she learned that canoe instructors do not allow tipping.

48. A gifted child with a large vocabulary and a penchant for puns, Lalo had used large words to tell his parents that when he grew up he wanted to become

a cook for a tribe of cannibals. His parents were disappointed because they thought that rather than becoming a "humanitarian, " he might want to become a vegetarian like them.

49. Ali was a lioness in a circus lion-taming act. The last act of the day had not gone well, and the lion tamer had hit Ali repeatedly with his whip to subdue her. Not seeing the chair the lion tamer used to help control her, Ali took advantage of the situation to maul the tamer. As a result of her actions, she was relegated to a cage at the zoo for the rest of her life.

50. The 120 degrees were college degrees which were being conferred in a shady park on the campus of a university. The temperature was actually quite pleasant on the delightful spring day.

51. Gwen's new baby kitten was entirely black except for a little patch of white hair under its chin. Before she had seen that patch of hair, she had wanted to name her kitten Midnight. Instead she named her cat "Eleven forty-five." Gwen nicknamed her cat "Quartertill."

52. To the local air-conditioned library.

53. He was Dr. Frankenstein, a fictional character who literally made new human beings from bits and pieces of dead bodies.

54. The woman was the doctor of a famous artist. She had just received the results of the artists medical tests and concluded that the artist would die soon of his illness. Realizing that the value of an artist's work often increases after his death, she took advantage of her information to cash in on the artist's

misfortune.

55. During a recent bank robbery the perpetrator had handed the teller a note threatening "to shot (sic) all of the customers and employees" if his directions were not followed. Police set up roadblocks to capture the suspect and administered a spelling test to people who matched the suspect's description, asking them to spell the word "shoot." The test worked, and the culprit was apprehended.

56. Funeral services for an eccentric owner of a movie theater.

57. The player was part of a foursome in a golf match. The other three members of the group were his business superiors. Even though he was a capable golfer, throughout the match he made it a point to miss enough putts to allow his bosses to win.

58. He was the coach of a professional ball team. The team's owner fired him because he was "sick and tired" of the team's dismal performance.

59. The woman was ticketed for driving alone in a freeway lane reserved for cars carrying more than one person. She argued that the law did not specify that the passengers had to be alive, therefore the body she was transporting in her hearse permitted her to use the car-pool lane. The judge agreed.

60. Producers posted this tongue-in-cheek advertisement for an actress to perform the part of an evil witch in their play.

61. The principal is the mother of three children. Calvin, her youngest is always the first to use the bath water every night and is jokingly referred to

as the "ringleader"—the person who begins the dirty ring that regularly forms in the tub. He is also so squirmy afterwards that she finds it difficult to pin a diaper on him.

62. An inept pair of burglars had become careless after a string of successful thefts. After dropping off his cohort for what would become their final heist, the driver took the getaway car to be washed. The police, summoned by a silent alarm, easily arrested the stranded burglar and later his accomplice.

63. As a finale to his show, the magician introduced to the audience his assistant, whom he had just sawed in two. As it turned out, the assistant was the magician's half-sister, a pun the audience found unbearable.

64. The men had been cheated while playing a game of blackjack (sometimes called 21). Both players had asked for hits (extra cards) and had received high-value cards with club symbols on them. They summoned the authorities when one of the players was dealt two aces of diamonds in the same hand. You see, there is supposed to be only one ace of diamonds in a legal deck of cards.